THE ESSENTIAL ELVIS

Exclusive Distributors:
MUSIC SALES LIMITED
8/9 Frith Street,
London W1V 5TZ, England.
MUSIC SALES PTY LIMITED
120 Rothschild Avenue,
Rosebery, NSW 2018,
Australia.

Order No.AM927872
ISBN 0-7119-4864-X

Music processed by Paul Ewers Music Design
Book design by Pearce Marchbank, Studio Twenty
Quarked by Ben May

Printed in the United Kingdom by
J.B. Offset Printers (Marks Tey) Limited, Marks Tey, Essex.

YOUR GUARANTEE OF QUALITY

As publishers, we strive to produce every book to
the highest commercial standards.
The music has been freshly engraved and the book has been carefully
designed to minimise awkward page turns and to make
playing from it a real pleasure.
Particular care has been given to specifying acid-free, neutral-sized
paper made from pulps which have not been elemental chlorine bleached.
This pulp is from farmed sustainable forests and was produced with
special regard for the environment.
Throughout, the printing and binding have been planned to ensure a
sturdy, attractive publication which should give years of enjoyment.
If your copy fails to meet our high standards, please inform us and
we will gladly replace it.

Music Sales' complete catalogue
describes thousands of titles and is available in
full colour sections by subject, direct from
Music Sales Limited.
Please state your areas of interest and send a
cheque/postal order for £1.50 for postage to:
Music Sales Limited, Newmarket Road,
Bury St. Edmunds, Suffolk IP33 3YB.

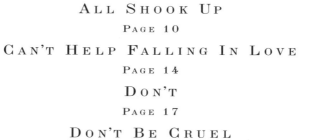

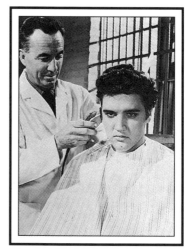

(You're So Square) Baby I Don't Care

Words & Music by Jerry Leiber & Mike Stoller.

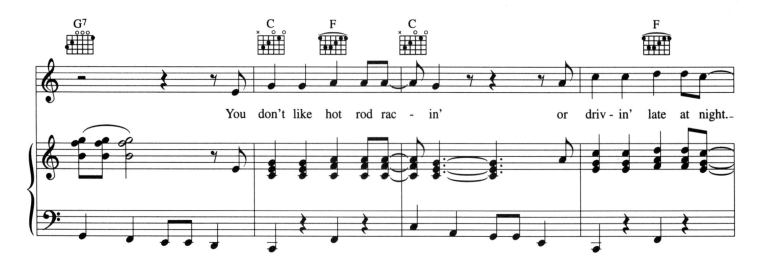

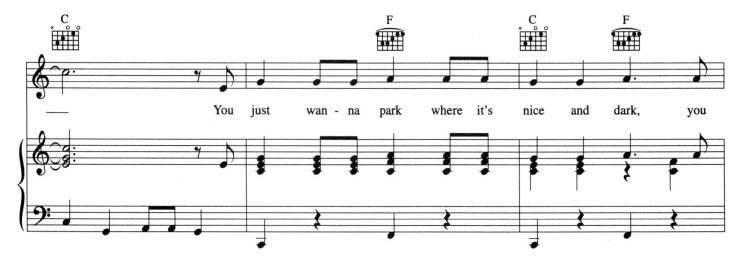

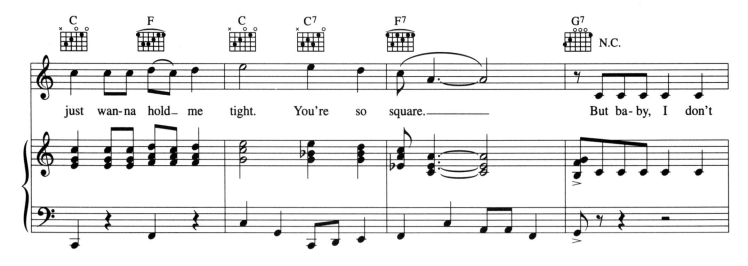

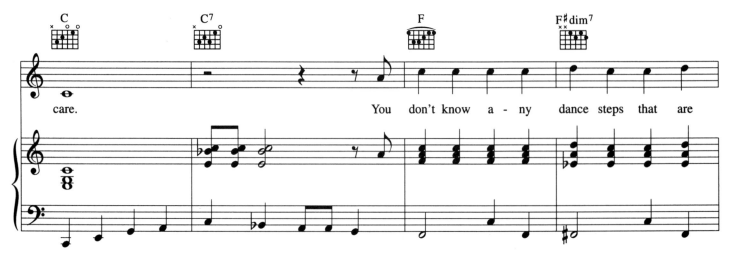

new,   but no one else can love me like you do.

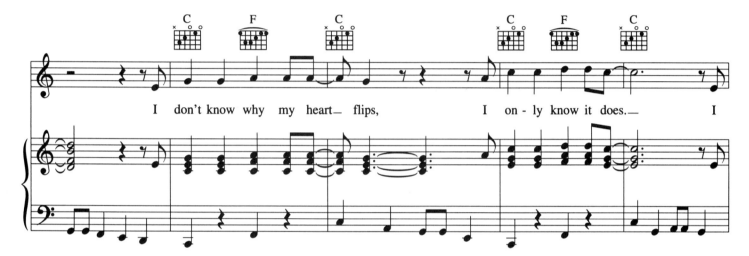

I don't know why my heart— flips,   I on-ly know it does.—   I

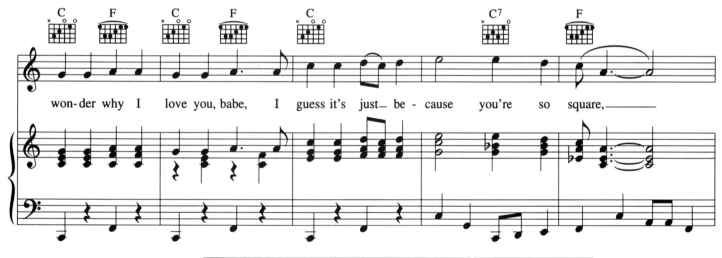

won-der why I love you, babe, I guess it's just— be-cause   you're so square,———

and ba-by, I don't care.   You   care.———

ALL SHOOK UP

WORDS & MUSIC BY OTIS BLACKWELL & ELVIS PRESLEY.

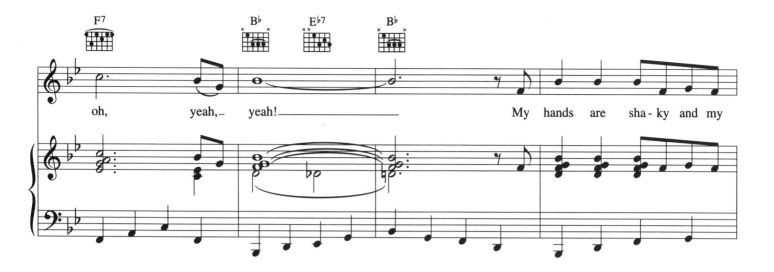

oh, yeah,— yeah!_____ My hands are sha-ky and my

knees are weak,— I can't seem to stand— on my own two feet,—

who do you thank when you have such luck?— I'm in love! I'm all shook up!— Mm—

mm, oh, oh, yeah,— yeah!_____

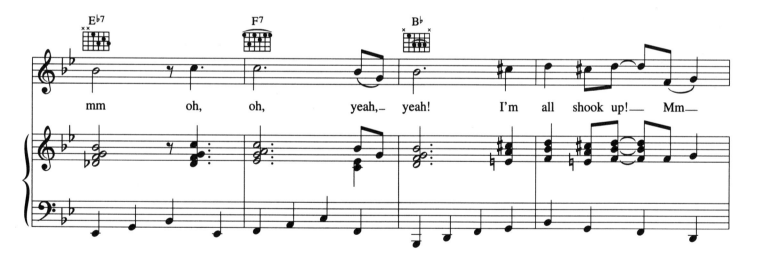

Can't Help Falling In Love

Words & Music by George Weiss, Hugo Peretti & Luigi Creatore.

love with you. Shall I

stay would it be a

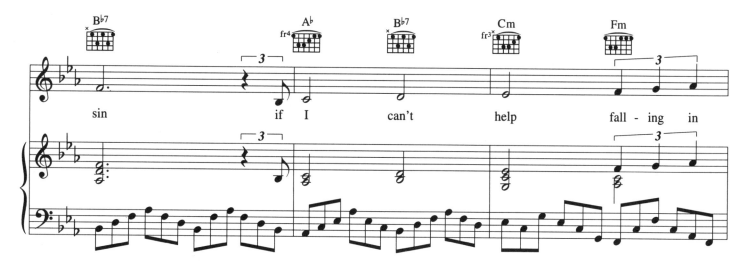

sin if I can't help fall - ing in

love with you. Like a ri - ver flows

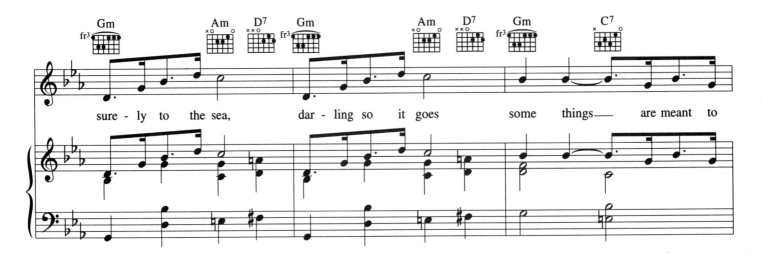

sure - ly to the sea, dar - ling so it goes some things___ are meant to

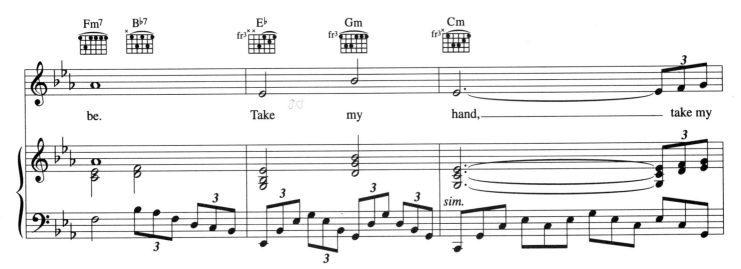

be. Take my hand,_____ take my

whole life too, for I can't

help fall - ing in love with you.

DON'T

WORDS & MUSIC BY JERRY LEIBER & MIKE STOLLER.

CHORUS

Don't, don't, that's what you
Don't, don't, leave my em-

say, each time that I hold you this way.
brace, for here in my arms is your place.

When I feel like this and I want to kiss you, ba-by, don't say
When the night grows cold and I want to hold you, ba-by, don't say

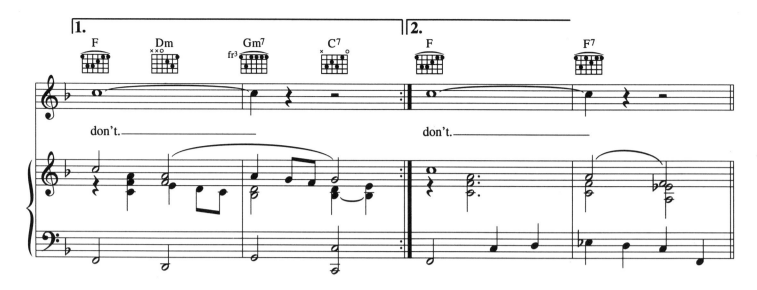

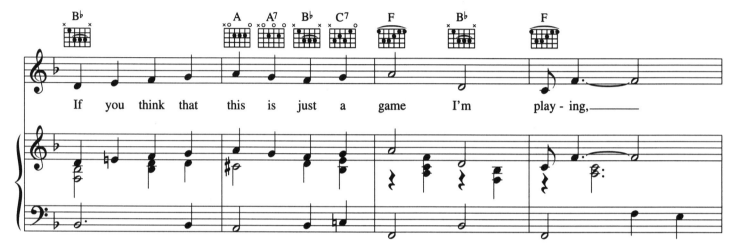

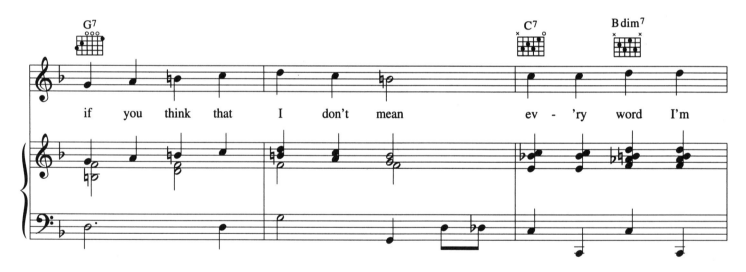

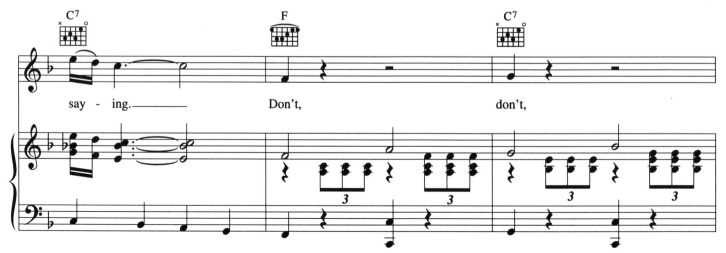

don't feel that way, I'm your love and yours I___ will

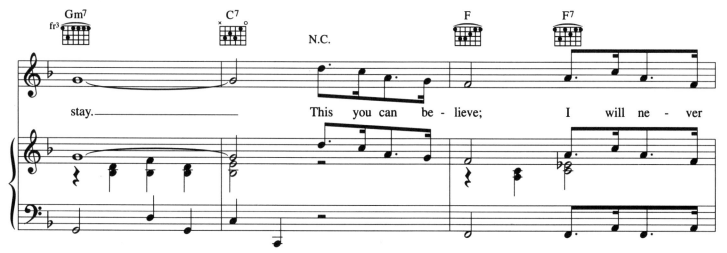

stay.___ This you can be-lieve; I will ne - ver

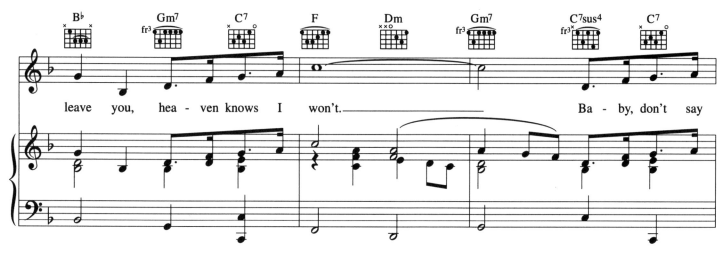

leave you, hea - ven knows I won't.___ Ba - by, don't say

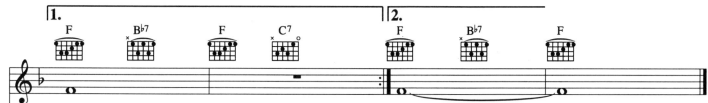

don't. don't.___

DON'T BE CRUEL

WORDS & MUSIC BY OTIS BLACKWELL & ELVIS PRESLEY.

Medium bright (with good beat)

You know I can be found— sit-ting home all a-
Ba-by if I made you mad for some-thing I might have said,—

lone, if you can't come a-round, at least, please te-le-
—— please let's for-get the past the fu-ture looks bright a-

phone. Don't be cruel——— to a heart that's true.———
head. Don't be cruel——— to a heart that's

true._____ I don't want no oth-er love, ba-by, it's just

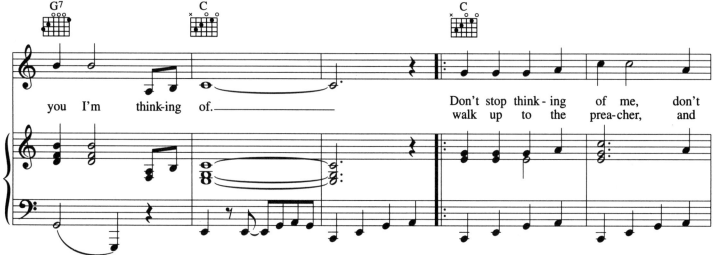

you I'm think-ing of._____ Don't stop think-ing of me, don't
walk up to the prea-cher, and

make me feel this way, come on o-ver here and love me, you know what I want you to
let us say "I do." Then you'll know you have me, and I'll know I'll have you

say. Don't be cruel_____ to a heart that's true._____ Why
too. Don't be cruel_____ to a heart that's true._____ I don't

Hard Headed Woman

Words & Music by Claude DeMetrius.

Bright rock

1. Well a hard head-ed wo-man, a soft heart-ed man
A - dam told Eve:— lis - ten here to me,

been the cause of trou-ble ev - er since the world be-gan.}
don't you let me catch you mess-in' 'round that ap-ple tree.}

Oh, yeah,—

ev - er since the world be - gan.___ Uh - huh - huh,___ a

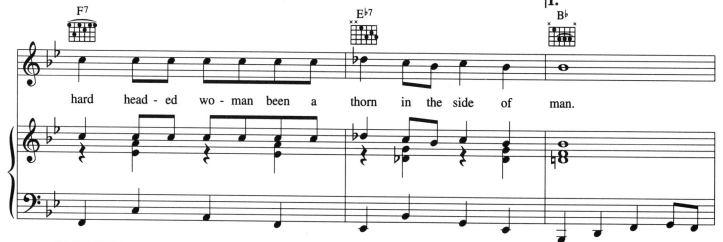

hard head - ed wo - man been a thorn in the side of man.

2. Now man.

3. Now
4. (I)
5. –

Sam - son told De - li - lah loud and clear,
heard 'bout a king___ who was do - in' swell
I got a wo - man, a head like a rock,

His Latest Flame (Marie's The Name)

Words & Music by Doc Pomus & Mort Shuman.

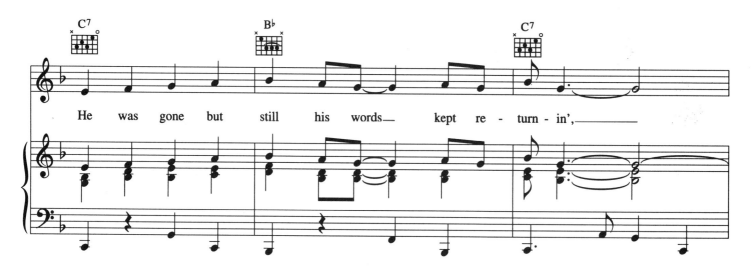

He was gone but still his words— kept re-turn-in',———

what else was there for me to do— but cry.

Would you be-lieve

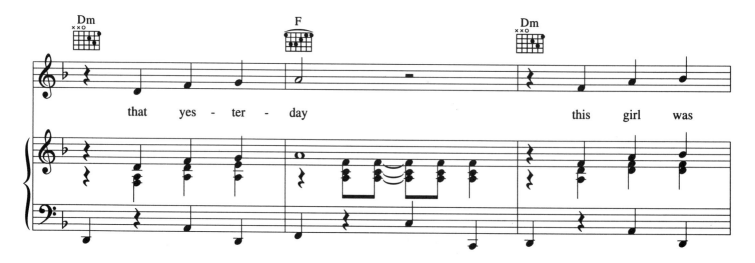

that yes-ter-day this girl was

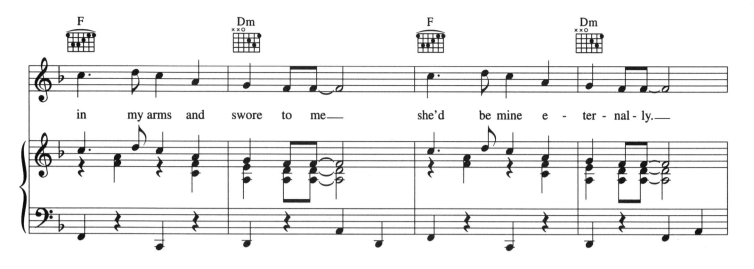

in my arms and swore to me ___ she'd be mine e - ter - nal - ly. ___

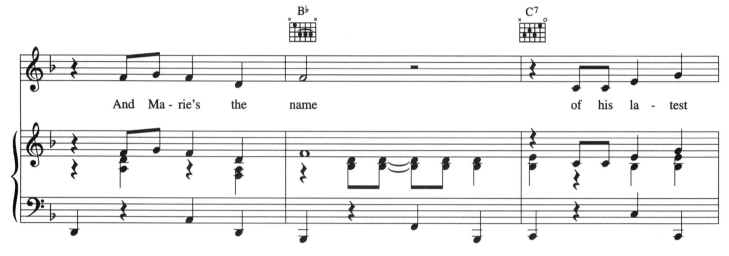

And Ma - rie's the name of his la - test

1. flame. A ve - ry old

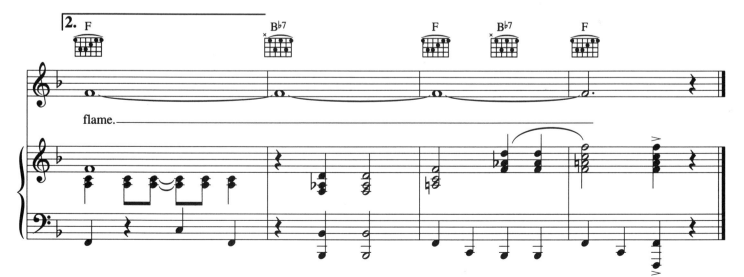

2. flame. ___

JAILHOUSE ROCK

WORDS & MUSIC BY JERRY LEIBER & MIKE STOLLER.

Medium bright rock

1. The war-den threw a par-ty in the
2. Spi-der Mur-phy play'd the te-nor
3. Num-ber For-ty se-ven said to

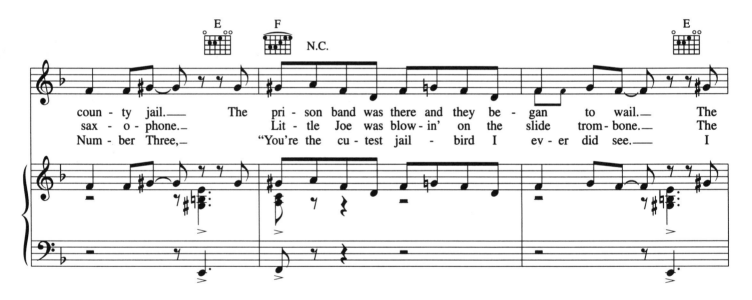

coun-ty jail.— The pri-son band was there and they be-gan to wail.— The
sax-o-phone.— Lit-tle Joe was blow-in' on the slide trom-bone.— The
Num-ber Three,— "You're the cu-test jail-bird I ev-er did see.— I

band was jump-in' and the joint be-gan to swing.— You should-'ve heard those knocked-out
drum-mer boy from Il-li-nois went crash, boom, bang!— The whole rhy-thm sec-tion was the
sure would be de-light-ed with your com-pa-ny.— Come on and do the jail-house

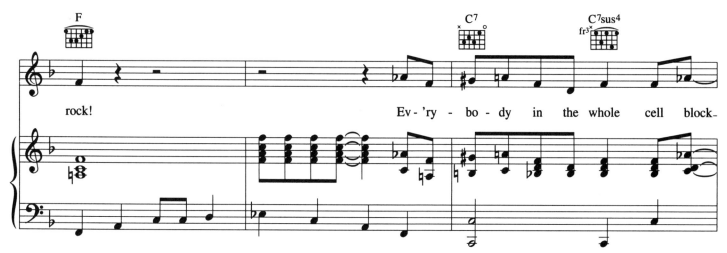

Verse 4:

The sad sack was a-sittin' on a block of stone,
Way over in the corner weepin' all alone.
The warden said, "Hey buddy, don't you be no square,
If you can't find a partner use a wooden chair!"
Let's rock *etc.*

Verse 5:

Shifty Henry said to Bugs, "For Heaven's sake,
No one's a lookin', now's our chance to make a break."
Bugsy turned to Shifty and he said, "Nix, nix,
I wanna stick around a while and get my kicks,"
Let's rock, *etc,*

LOVE ME TENDER

WORDS & MUSIC BY ELVIS PRESLEY & VERA MATSON.

Moderately slow

VERSE

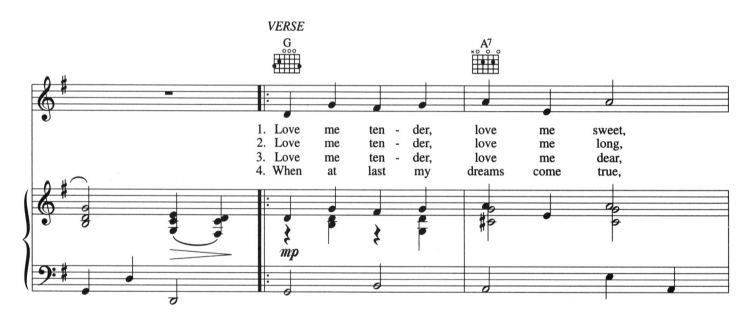

1. Love me ten - der, love me sweet,
2. Love me ten - der, love me long,
3. Love me ten - der, love me dear,
4. When at last my dreams come true,

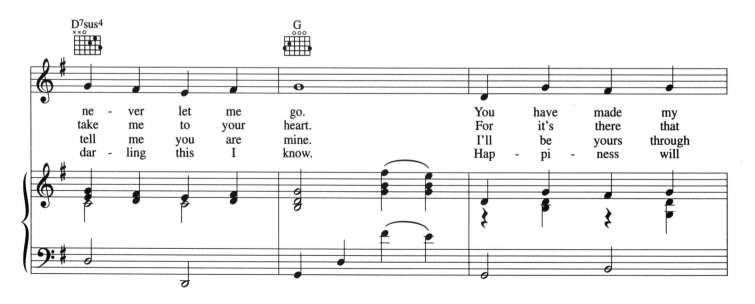

ne - ver let me go. You have made my
take me to your heart. For it's made there that
tell me you are mine. I'll be yours through
dar - ling this I know. Hap - pi - ness will

MEAN WOMAN BLUES
WORDS & MUSIC BY CLAUDE DEMETRIUS.

Medium rock

CHORUS

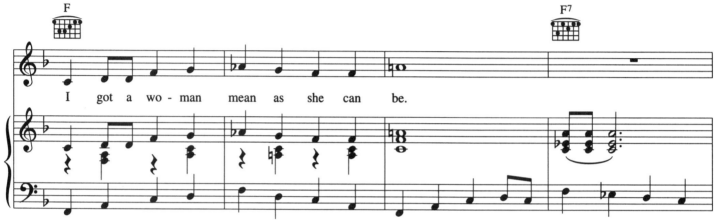

I got a wo-man mean as she can be.

I got a wo-man mean as she can be. Some-times I think she's

al - most mean as me.
1. A black cat up and
(2.) kiss so hard she
(3.) stran - gest gal I
4. She makes love with -

My Baby Left Me

Words & Music by Arthur Crudup.

Moderately bright

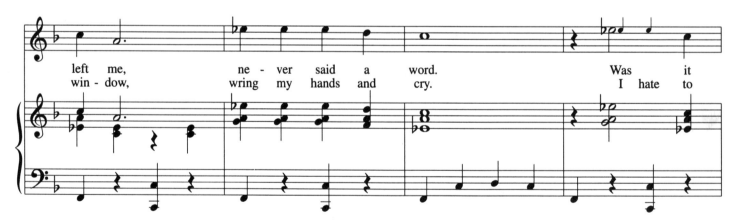

my ba - by left me. My ba - by ev - en
yes, she___ left me. My ba - by ev - en

left me,___ ne - ver said a word.___
left me,___ ne - ver said a word.___

2. Now I

Verse 3:

Baby, one of these mornings', Lord, it won't be long,
You'll look for me and, baby, and Daddy he'll be gone.
You know you left me, you know you left me.
My baby even left me, never said goodbye.

Verse 4:

Now, I stand at my window, wring my hands and moan.
All I know is that the one I love is gone.
My baby left me, you know she left me.
My baby even left me, never said a word.

KING CREOLE

WORDS & MUSIC BY JERRY LEIBER & MIKE STOLLER.

Bright rock

VERSE

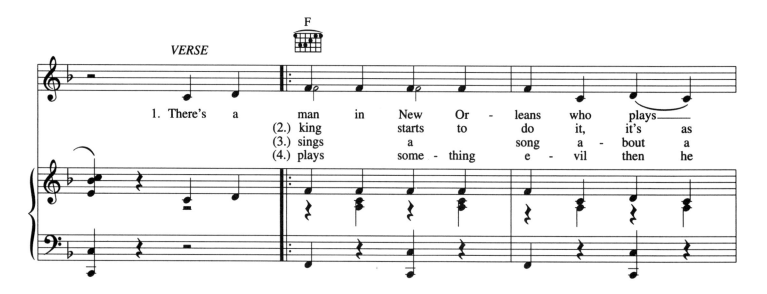

1. There's a man in New Or - leans who plays_____
(2.) king starts to do it, it's as
(3.) sings a song a - bout a
(4.) plays some - thing e - vil then he

rock and roll._____ He's a gui - tar_____ man
good as done._____ He_____ holds his gui -
craw - - dad hole._____ He_____ sings a
plays some - thing sweet. No_____ mat - ter what he

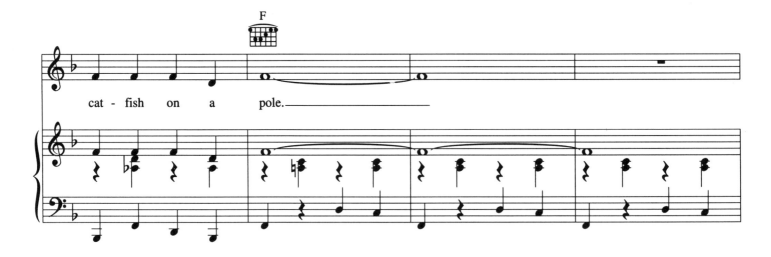

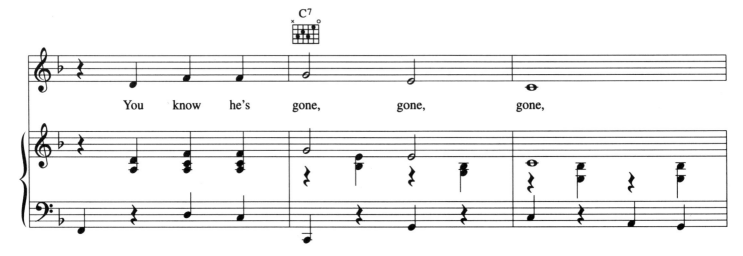

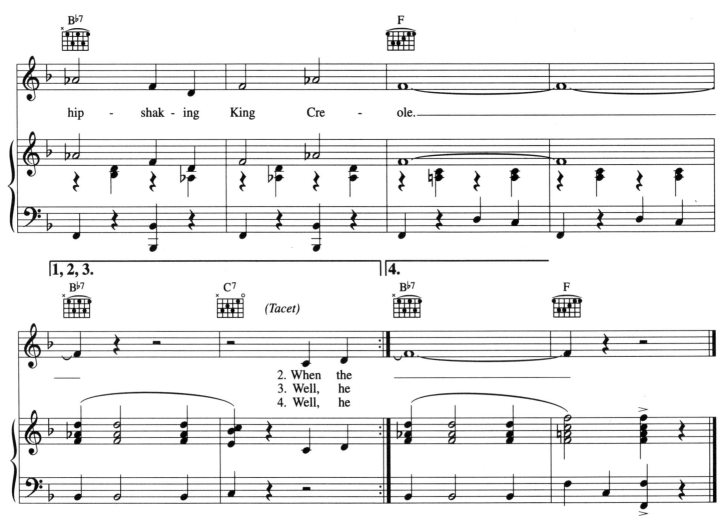

PARALYZED

WORDS & MUSIC BY OTIS BLACKWELL & ELVIS PRESLEY.

Bright shuffle

1. When you looked in-to my eyes, I
2. When we kissed, ooh, what a thrill. You

stood there like I was hyp-no-tised. You
took my hand and ooh, ba-by, what a chill. I

sent a feel-ing to my spine, a feel-ing warm and smooth and fine, but
felt like grab-bin' you real tight, squeeze and squeeze with all my might, but

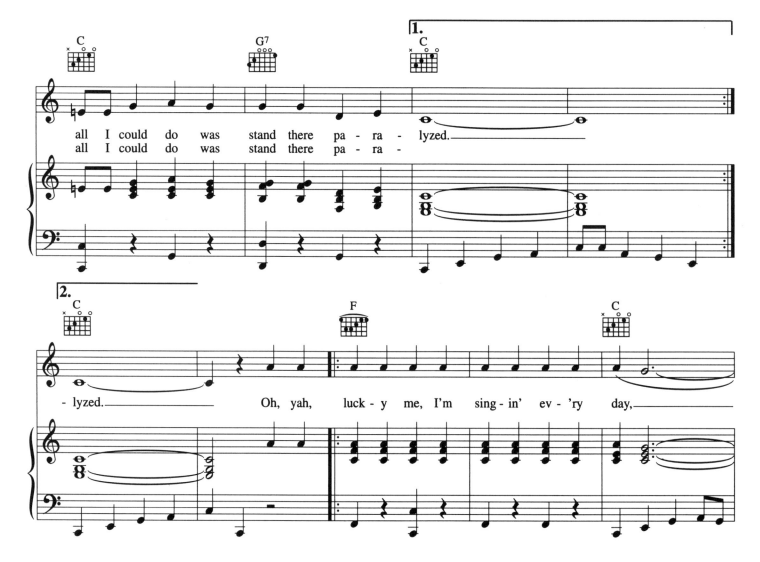

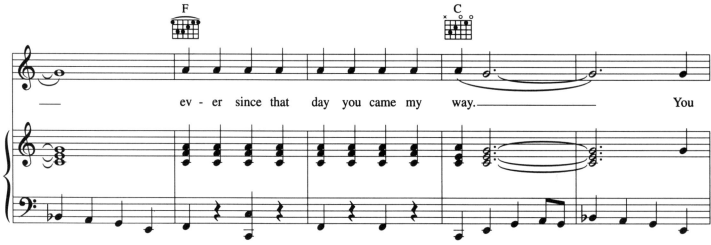

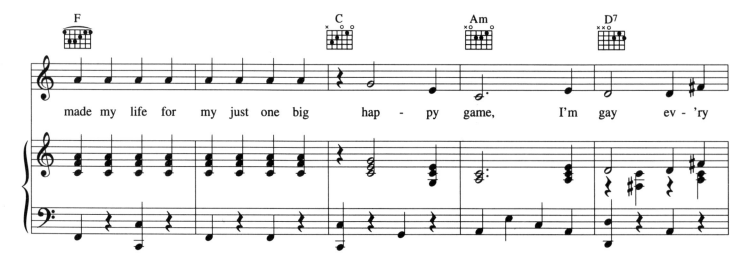

She's Not You

Words & Music by Jerry Leiber, Mike Stoller & Doc Pomus.

Moderately

Her hair is soft and her eyes are, oh, so blue. She's all the things a girl should be, but she's not you. She knows just

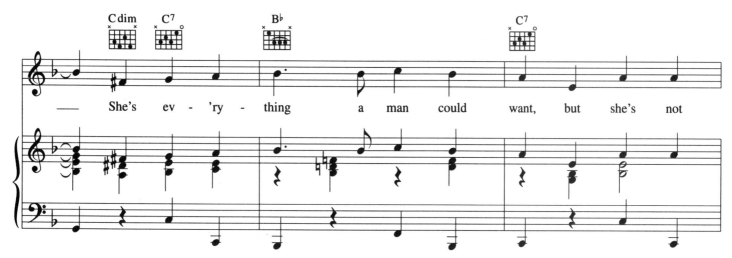

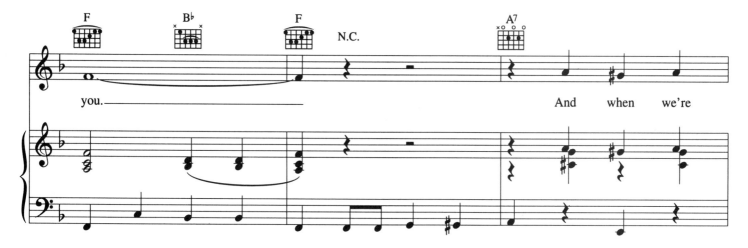

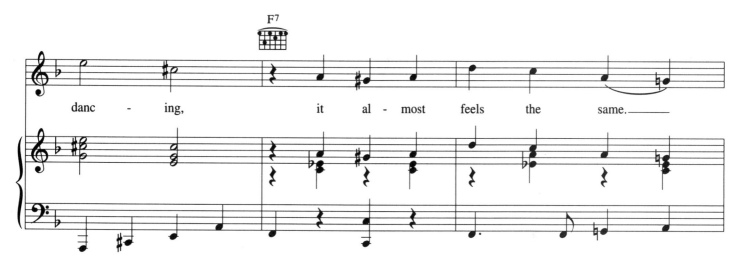

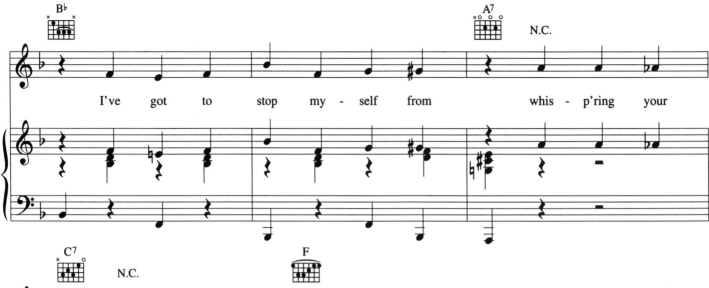

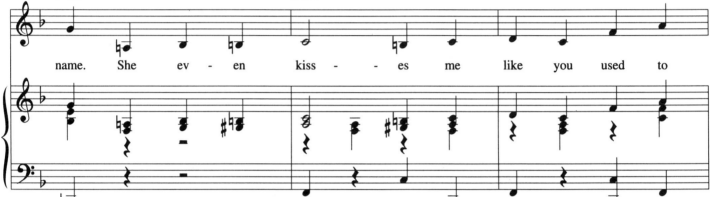

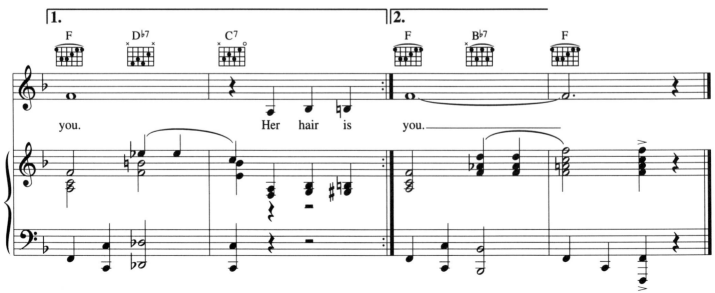

Stuck On You

Words & Music by Aaron Schroeder & J. Leslie McFarland.

1. You can shake an ap-ple off an ap-ple tree.
2. Gon-na run my fin-gers thru' your long black hair.

Shake a shake-a, su-gar, but you'll ne-ver shake me. Uh-uh-uh.
Squeeze you tight-er than a griz-zly bear. Uh-huh-huh.

No sir-ee, uh-uh. I'm gon-na
Yes sir-ee, uh-huh. I'm gon-na

stick like glue,——
stick like glue,——
stick be-cause I'm
stick be-cause I'm
stuck on
stuck on

1. you.

2. you. Hide in the kit-chen, hide in the hall.

Ain't gon - na do you no good at all.—— 'Cause once I catch ya and the

kiss-in' starts.—— A team o' wild hor - ses could - n't tear us a-part.

Try to take a ti-ger from his dad-dy's side.— That's— how— love is gon-na

keep us tied.— Uh-huh-huh.— Yes sir-ee,— uh-huh.—

I'm gon-na stick like glue,—

Yay, yay,— be-cause I'm stuck on you. you.

(Let Me Be Your) Teddy Bear

Words & Music by Kal Mann & Bernie Lowe.

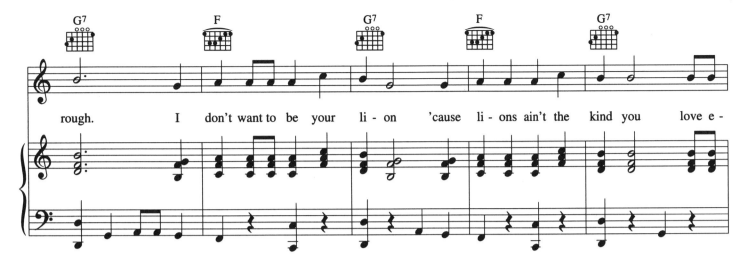

rough. I don't want to be your li - on 'cause li - ons ain't the kind you love e -

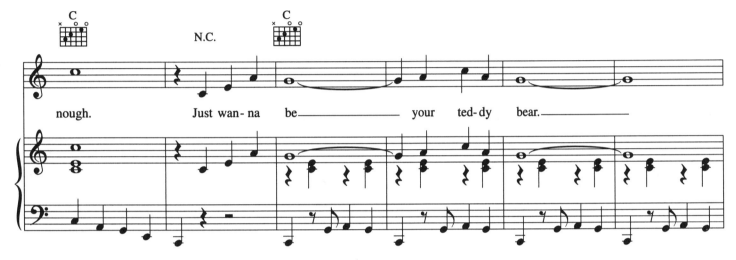

nough. Just wan - na be_____ your ted - dy bear._____

Put a chain a - round my neck_ and lead me a - ny - where. Oh, let me be_____

1.

___ your ted - dy bear.

2.

bear._____

WOODEN HEART

WORDS & MUSIC BY FRED WISE, BEN WEISMAN, KAY TWOMEY & BERTHOLD KAEMPFERT.

Moderately (in 'Two')

Can't you see I love you, please don't break my heart in two, that's not hard to

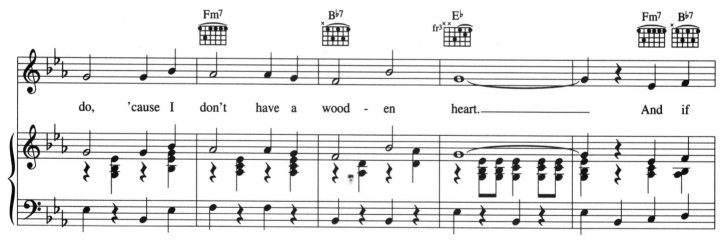

do, 'cause I don't have a wood-en heart. And if

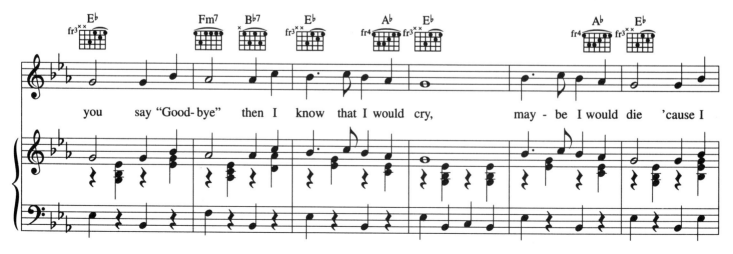

you say "Good-bye" then I know that I would cry, may-be I would die 'cause I

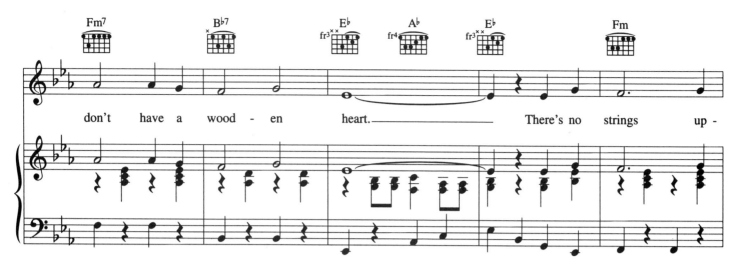

don't have a wood - en heart. _____ There's no strings up -

on this love of mine, it was al - ways you from the start, _____

— treat me nice, treat me good, treat me like you real - ly should, 'cause

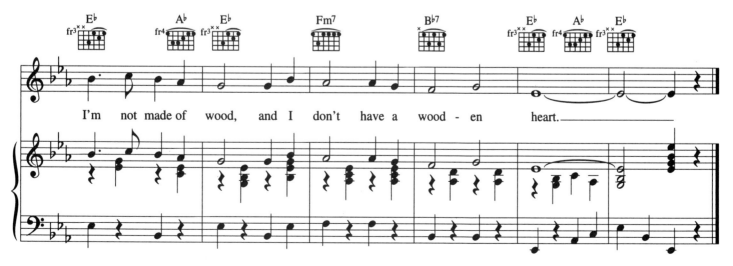

I'm not made of wood, and I don't have a wood - en heart. _____

Return To Sender

Words & Music by Otis Blackwell & Winfield Scott.

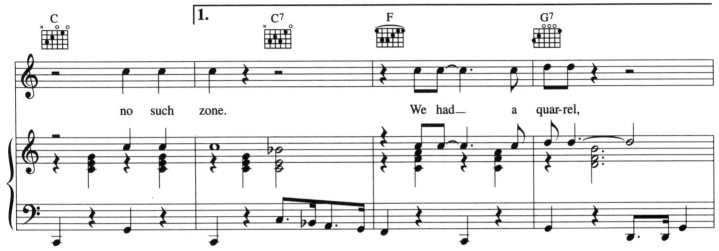

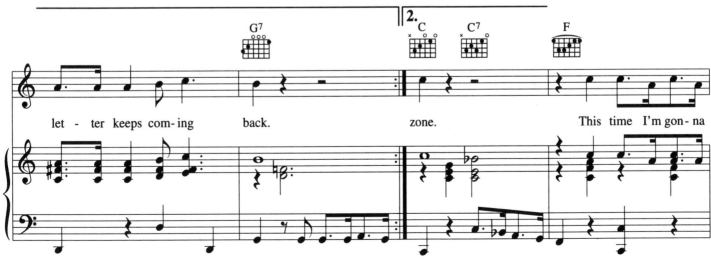

take it my-self and put it right in her hand. And if it comes back the

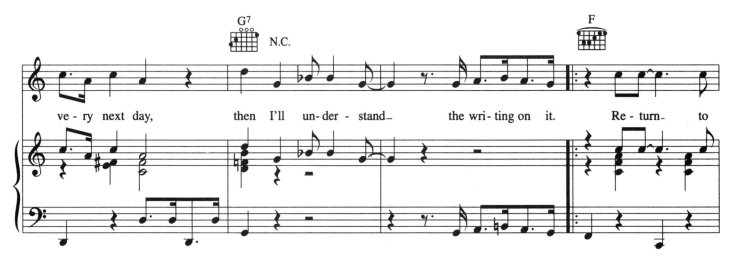

ve - ry next day, then I'll un-der-stand the wri-ting on it. Re-turn to

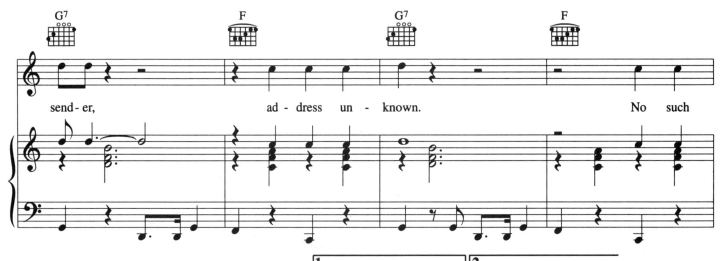

send - er, ad - dress un - known. No such

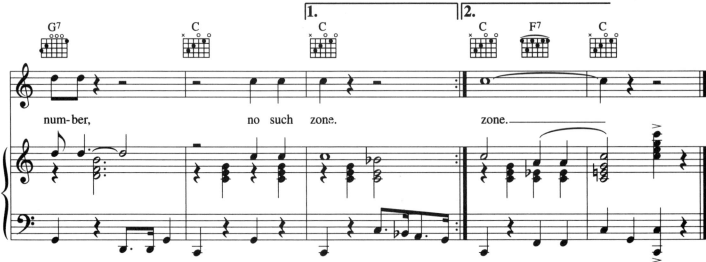

1.

num-ber, no such zone.

2.

zone.